The 'Safe Use of Small Arms' Series ...G
Collection & Research Association t ...le
information for an individual to be comp ...s.
This book forms part of a wider system ...g ...u must not be used in
isolation.

Version 1.0

For amendments and updates, refer to https://vickersmg.blog/product/safe-use-of-small-arms-lee-enfield-rifles/

Written by Jacob McBride.

The Safe Use of Small Arms Series Editor is Richard Fisher.
Book design and layout by Richard Fisher and Matt Yates.
Photo contributions by Jacob McBride, Lee-Enfield Rifle Association and Jay Lynch.

Thanks to the committee of the Lee-Enfield Rifle Association and Mike Burns (Bloke on the Range) for taking the time to review the text contained within this book. Any remaining errors or omissions are the Association's responsibility.

ISBN 978-1-9168917-7-7

Published by the Vickers MG Collection & Research Association
www.vickersmg.org

SAFE USE OF SMALL ARMS

Lee-Enfield Rifles

INTRODUCTION

This document sets out the knowledge requirements for the above qualification. Each section includes the Learning Outcome and Assessment Criteria as identified in the Defence Awarding Organisation Qualification Handbook (QN: 601/5942/X)[1]. It should be noted that this is not an accredited qualification at the present time; however, it has been built on a recognised standard so that future compatibility may be permitted if it becomes accredited. The structure of the book is based upon this qualification and does not reflect the order in which training should be taught. The suggested order of teaching is given in Appendix 3.

It should be noted that the drills contained in this book are intended to satisfy both civilian and military organisations running ranges, which may be adapted by local range rules. Modern requirements may not be fully compatible with historic small arms and where they are not suitable, the range conducting officer needs to be aware of adapted or incompatible drills. Furthermore, we use the terms 'firearm' and 'weapon' interchangeably which reflects the historic and military nature of the content.

The knowledge section has been created by the Vickers MG Collection & Research Association and provides all of the information, or references to where the information can be found, for the Assessment Criteria to be satisfied.

---

[1] Defence Awarding Organisation, *Qualification Handbook Level 2 Award in Safe Use of Personal Weapons The Qualification* (Shrivenham: Ministry of Defence, 2015) <https://www.gov.uk/government/publications/dao-qualification-handbooks-level-2-courses>.

The fourth heading in each section identifies how the learner may demonstrate their knowledge. Theoretical sections may, generally, be proven through written or verbal explanation, or presentation. The weapon may not always be required for these sections. Where 'demonstration' is identified, the learner will require access to a weapon; however, in some cases this can be a drill purpose or deactivated example with moving parts.[2] Additional equipment needed for the lesson is also identified. Demonstration may also incorporate a supervised firing demonstration.

The QR code on each page links to an instructional video to that Element. This is available through subscription to the online element of the course.

GLOSSARY

Authority Holder	The named individual(s) that hold the legal authority to possess the weapons being used.
MOA	Minute of Angle
NSPs	Normal Safety Precautions
Range Conducting Officer	The qualified person that is conducting any range activity where the weapons are being used.

REFERENCES

The majority of this information has been sourced from official publications and selected extracts copied where appropriate. Some words and phrases have been changed for consistency and supplemented with additional information as required. Those used directly are identified as footnotes with the text.

---

[2] If a deactivated weapon is used, it will be necessary for the assessor to verify that it is suitable for the assessment to be completed.

Firearms Covered

This document covers the following common types of Lee-Enfield Rifles (this list is not exhaustive and is representative of common models that may be encountered):

Rifle	Calibre	Reference Image
No.1 Mk.1 (*,**,***)	.303	
No.1 Mk.III	.303	
No.1 MK.III Sniper	.303	
No.1 Mk.III*/2A/2A1 (No.1 Mk.III pictured)	.303 / 7.62	
No.2 Mk.IV	.22	
No.4 Mk.1	.303	

Rifle	Calibre	Reference Image
No.4 Mk.1 (T)	.303	
No.4 Mk.1*/No.4 Mk.1/3 (No.4 Mk.1* pictured)	.303	
No.4 Mk.2/No.4 Mk.1/2 (No.4 Mk.2 pictured)	.303	
No.5 Mk.1	.303	
No.7 Mk.1	.22	
No.8 Mk.1	.22	

Rifle	Calibre	Reference Image
N9 Mk.1	.22	
L39A1/7.62 CONV/Envoy (7.62 CONV pictured)	7.62	
L42A1	7.62	
Enforcer	7.62	

CONTENTS

1.1 GENERIC

The learner will: **Understand the safety implications when handling weapons and ammunition**

The learner can: **Explain the importance of following recognised Normal Safety Precautions (NSPs) when using weapons**

The learner knows:

☑ Handle

☑ Use

☑ Competent

- Why it is important to use NSPs.
    - o PRIMARY:
        - ▪ To take a weapon from an unknown or unsafe state and place it in a known safe state.
    - o SECONDARY:
        - ▪ To show others that the weapon is safe.
        - ▪ To ensure that weapons are in a mechanically fit state to be stored.
        - ▪ To check the state of a weapon.
- The organisation's procedures for when NSPs should be conducted are:
    - o When removing a weapon from storage.
    - o When placing a weapon into storage.
    - o When a weapon has been out of sight or reach of the person then handling the weapon.
    - o When there is a suspicion (reasonable or otherwise) that the state of the weapon is unknown (for example, this could include forgetfulness or a moment of lapsed thought on the part of the holder and they wish to check the state of the weapon).
    - o At any time the weapon is being taken into the possession of another person (under UK law, possession is any handling regardless of time held).

The learner can demonstrate this by:

Verbal explanation, written description, or online test if available.

To teach this lesson, the trainer needs:

- No special equipment.

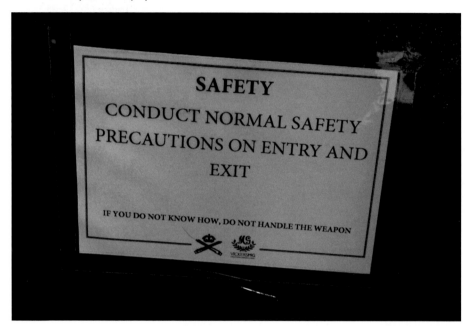

1.2 GENERIC

The learner will: **Understand the safety implications when handling weapons and ammunition**

The learner can: **Explain the declaration and consequences for the unauthorised removal of ammunition and casings from a range**

☑ Handle

☑ Use

☑ Competent

NOTE: This is primarily focussed at military training and military ranges; however, there are specific UK legal requirements, and it is good, safe, practice to understand what ammunition being taken from a range or demonstration area.

The learner knows:

There is a UK legal requirement to ensure that no person takes any ammunition which they are not permitted to possess. For example, ball ammunition and primed cases are restricted to those with authorisation or firearms certificates that cover those items. Other countries or regions may regulate blank ammunition as well.

Any spent cases, which people may be permitted to possess, must be checked that they are truly spent and free-from-explosive content (see Unit 2.6).

All ball ammunition MUST be accounted for on either a Firearms Certificate or the Registered Firearms Dealer Register. Deviations from this may cause the holder to possess illegally.

All individuals must check their pockets, bags, cases, pouches, and any other items to ensure they do not take anything they are not authorised to possess.

The British Army procedure for declarations is part of Pamphlet 21 (2-47 to 2-54, September 2020 issue)[3].

The learner can demonstrate this by:

Verbal explanation, written description, or online test if available.

To teach this lesson, the trainer needs:

- No special equipment.

---

[3] Ministry Of Defence, *Pamphlet 21: Training Regulations for Armoured Fighting Vehicles, Infantry Weapon Systems and Pyrotechnics*, Close Combat - Ranges, 3rd edn (Warminster: Ministry of Defence, 2021).

1.3 GENERIC

The learner will: **Understand the safety implications when handling weapons and ammunition.**

The learner can: **Explain the organisation's reporting procedure for defective weapons and ancillaries.**

☑ Handle

☑ Use

The learner knows:

☑ Competent

That any defective weapon (or ancillary) must be recorded on the log sheet for the weapon (example in Appendix 2) and the Authority Holder must be informed and a full report made. Additional reporting forms may be required depending on the circumstances. For example, if the weapon has been subject to Ministry of Defence Non-Service Pattern Light Weapon inspection, a record of it may be made on the history sheet. If the organisation has its own record keeping, this should be completed as well.

The report should include:

- How the weapon was being used.
- What ammunition, if any, was being used.
- What is believed to have happened.
- Whether any stoppage was observed and what immediate action was applied.
- Whether any parts were replaced.
- If the weapon continued to be used.

Defective ammunition must be stored away from all other spent casings or live ammunition. As with defective weapons, it must be reported to the authority holder and include:

- The manufacturer.

- The batch.
- A description of how it was being used.
- Any damage caused to the weapon, ancillaries or any injuries to persons.

If being used on a managed range, the Range Conducting Officer must be informed, and the local procedures followed as necessary. This may include reports as described above.

The learner can demonstrate this by:

Verbal explanation, written description, or online test if available.

To teach this lesson, the trainer needs:

- Example inspection and firing record sheets.

1.4 GENERIC

The learner will: **Understand the safety implications when handling weapons and ammunition.**

The learner can: **Explain the importance of the Weapon Handling Test (WHT).**

☑ Handle

The learner knows:

☑ Use

That a WHT is key to demonstrating the handler's competence in using a weapon. It shows their understanding and competence at the time of the test, and it can be reasonably assumed that they will remain competent for a period after.

☑ Competent

The period will depend on the frequency of use of the weapon and level of exposure they have as a handler to it. For example, a weapon type infrequently handled will have the user's familiarity with it expire more quickly than that of a weapon they use more frequently.

General WHTs are conducted on an annual basis but the above note should be applied. Again, for example, if a handler has not used a weapon for 9 months, then, even if the WHT is within one year, it is likely they would not be considered currently competent. This should be considered on a case-by-case and risk basis.

The relevant WHTs can be found in Appendix 4 of this book.

The learner can demonstrate this by:

Verbal explanation, written description, or online test if available.

To teach this lesson, the trainer needs:

- Example training record sheets.

1.5 Lee-Enfield Rifles

The learner will: **Understand the safety implications when handling weapons and ammunition.**

The learner can: **Pick up the weapon and make it safe.**

☑ Handle

The learner knows:

☑ Use

The Normal Safety Precautions for the Lee-Enfield Rifles and can demonstrate those.

☑ Competent

REFER TO NSPs for Lee-Enfield Rifles – Appendix 1.

The learner can demonstrate this by:

Weapons Handling Test 1.

To teach this lesson, the trainer needs:

- Live, drill purpose or suitable deactivated firearm.
- (optional) Drill rounds.
- Lee-Enfield Rifles Aide Memoire.

1.6 Lee-Enfield Rifles

The learner will: **Understand the safety implications when handling weapons and ammunition.**

The learner can: **Handover/takeover the weapon in a safe condition.**

☑ Handle

The learner knows:

☑ Use

That to handover or takeover a weapon in a safe condition, they are required to conduct the Normal Safety Precautions for the Lee-Enfield rifles in the presence of the transferor or transferee and can demonstrate those.

☑ Competent

Person with the weapon (transferor) conducts NSPs 1 to 5.

Person receiving the weapon (transferee) conducts NSPs 1 and 4 to 9.

REFER TO NSPs for Lee-Enfield Rifles – Appendix 1.

The learner can demonstrate this by:

Demonstration (drill purposes or moving parts deactivated suitable) or online test if available.

To teach this lesson, the trainer needs:

- Live, drill purpose or suitable deactivated firearm.
- (optional) Drill rounds.

2.1 Lee-Enfield Rifles

The learner will: **Understand the characteristics of the weapon.**

The learner can: **Conduct NSPs in line with organisational procedures.**

The learner knows:

☑ Handle

That they are required to conduct NSPs when they take the Lee-Enfield rifle from any storage, have been absent from it at any point or at the start of any period working with the weapon.

☑ Use

☑ Competent

REFER TO NSPs for Lee-Enfield Rifles – Appendix 1.

The learner can demonstrate this by:

Weapons Handling Test 1.

To teach this lesson, the trainer needs:

- Live, drill purpose or suitable deactivated firearm.
- (optional) Drill rounds.

Chamber flag inserted on L42A1

2.2 Lee-Enfield Rifles

The learner will: **Understand the characteristics of the weapon.**

The learner can: **Explain characteristics of the weapon.**

The learner knows:

The main characteristics of the Lee-Enfield Rifles are:

☒ Handle

☒ Use

☑ Competent

- Reliability: The Lee-Enfield rifle is known for its robustness and reliability, capable of functioning effectively in harsh conditions
- Speed: They are renowned for their fast bolt-action mechanism, allowing for rapid cycling of rounds. This feature makes them particularly effective in situations requiring quick follow-up shots
- Versatility: The Lee-Enfield is a versatile weapon suitable for various roles, including infantry use, sniping, and cadet training in small-bore and full-bore varieties
- Magazine Capacity: The Lee-Enfield typically has a larger magazine capacity compared to other contemporary bolt-action rifles, often holding ten rounds in its magazine where others typically had five

The learner can demonstrate this by:

Verbal explanation, written description, or online test if available.

To teach this lesson, the trainer needs:

- No special equipment.

2.3 Lee-Enfield Rifles

The learner will: **Understand the characteristics of the weapon.**

The learner can: **Explain the main working parts of the weapon.**

The learner knows:

The names and location of the main working parts of the Lee-Enfield rifles. They need to know this ahead of the later elements and to ensure that they are correctly referring to parts when identifying stoppages, conducting immediate action, stripping, assembling and cleaning the Lee-Enfield rifles.

☒ Handle

☒ Use

☑ Competent

Whilst identifying the parts, the learner should be able briefly explain their function. By doing so, they will be able to understand the potential causes of stoppages and the operation of the rifle.

There are several groups made up of numerous parts.

- Bolt
    - o Bolt body, this contains the striker spring and striker as well as provisions to accept the bolt head by a female thread
    - o Cocking piece, this is typically either a 'button' shape (earlier rifles) or 'square' pattern which typically contains serrations for grip in adverse conditions
    - o Bolt head, this contains the extractor and extractor spring and has a male thread on the back to thread into the bolt body
- Magazine
    - o Magazine body which contains the magazine spring and follower

- Magazine follower and spring, these are attached as one unit typically by rivets and control the feed of ammunition
- Barrel, a steel tube closed at one end by the bolt, provided with a chamber for containing a cartridge and helical grooves for causing the bullet to spin upon firing
- Foresight, for aiming
- Rear Sight, for aiming, typically distance adjustable in the form of a ladder, tangent or two position flip sight. Tangent sights found on No.1 rifle from Mk.1 to Mk.3*. When a ladder sight is used there is often a fixed aperture battle sight (this is ground off on No.4 Mk.1(T) and L42A1 rifles to allow the fitment of the No.32 and L1A1 telescope respectively)
- Receiver
  - Charger guide, directs the feed of ammunition into the magazine from a charger
  - Magazine cut-off, towards the beginning of its inclusion was to control the rate of fire by allowing for only single loading of ammunition when in the closed position and rapid fire feeding from the magazine when open. Later on, the cut-off was not to be used for single loading but to allow the magazine to be charged without inserting a cartridge in to the chamber or to be able to unload the rifle while still retaining any cartridges that may remain in the magazine (present on some No.1 rifles and very rarely on later rifles)
  - Bolt release catch, sprung element to retain the bolt head on No.1 rifles
  - Bolt release button, depressed to allow removal of the bolt from the receiver (present on the No.4 Mk.1, 1/2, Mk.2, No.5, No.7-N9, L42A1, Enforcer)
  - Rear sight (on a No.4/5 based receiver)
  - Magazine catch, located within the trigger guard is depressed to allow removal of the magazine from the receiver

The learner can demonstrate this by:

Verbal explanation, written description, or online test if available.

To teach this lesson, the trainer needs:

- Live, drill purpose or suitable deactivated firearm.
- Training documentation such as posters displaying the internal operating mechanism.
- (optional) Skeletonised firearm.

The following diagrams[4] identify the main components.

---

[4] Air Ministry, *Small Arms and Ground Defence Weapons: Part 1 Leading Particulars and General Information. Part 3 Fault Diagnosis,* (Air Ministry, 1954), Chapter 5: Rifle, .303 in., No. 1, Mk. 3*.

No.1 Rifle:

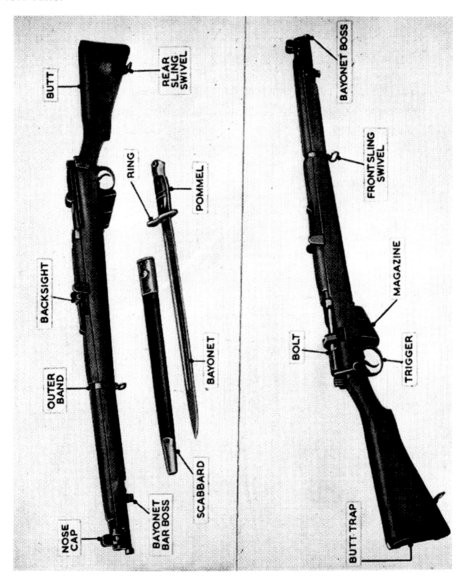

No. 4 Rifle:

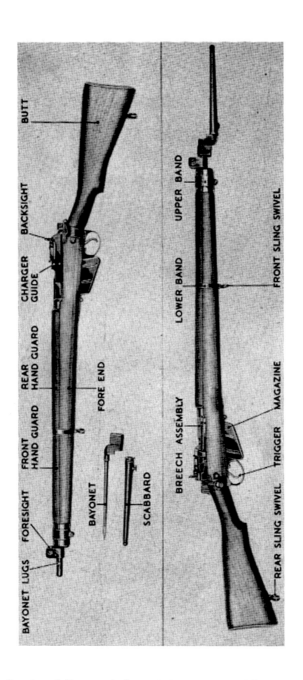

2.4 Lee-Enfield Rifles

The learner will: **Understand the characteristics of the weapon.**

The learner can: **Explain the weapon sighting system.**

The learner knows:

☒ Handle

There are multiple types of sight used with the Lee-Enfield Rifles:

☑ Use

☑ Competent

	No.1 Mk.1	No.1 Mk.III-MK.III*	No.4 - N9 Mk.1	No.4 Mk.1(T)	L42A1
Open Sights	X	X			
Aperture Sights			X	X	X
PPCo, Aldis, Winchester etc		X			
No.32 Mk.1-3				X	
L1A1					X
S&B PM1 (Various)					X

	Reference Image
Open Sights	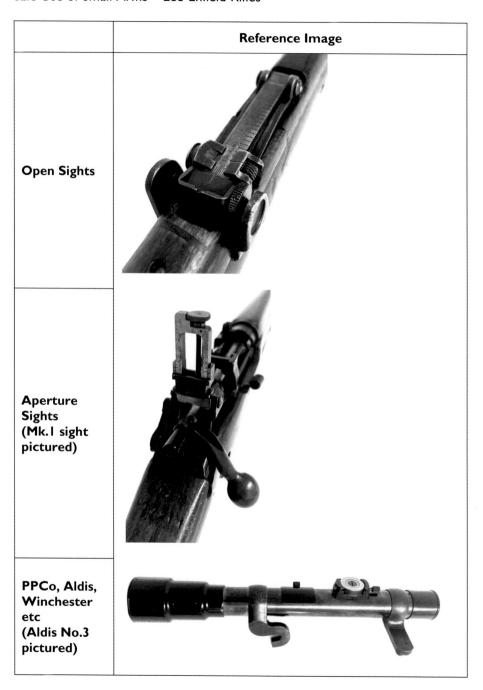
Aperture Sights (Mk.1 sight pictured)	
PPCo, Aldis, Winchester etc (Aldis No.3 pictured)	

No.32 Mk.1-3/L1A1 (No.32 Mk.3 pictured)	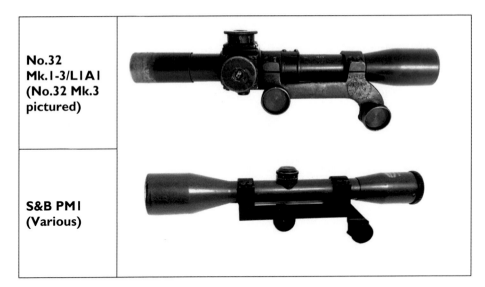
S&B PM1 (Various)	

The three most commonly encountered types of sight will be the open sights of the No.1 Mk.1 - Mk.III*, the aperture sights of the No.4-9 rifles and the No.32/L1A1 telescope found on the No.4 Mk.1(T) and L42A1 rifles.

The open sights on the No.1 Mk.1 – Mk.III* are tangent style fitted to the barrel of the rifle and are adjusted on a sliding scale from 200-2000 yards. Some earlier models of the sights have windage adjustment via a knob located on the right-hand side of the sight opening.

The sights on the No.4 Mk.1 – N9 Mk.1 are aperture sights and are mounted to the receiver of the rifle, have a fixed 300 yard battle sight (this is ground off on the No.4 MK.1(T) and L42A1 rifles in order for the No.32 and L1A1 scope respectively to be mounted) and are adjusted from 200-1300 yards. There are some exceptions to this; the sights for the No.5 Mk.1 go from 200-800 yards. The sight graduations also vary on the smallbore training rifles. No.7 has a normal No.4 rear sight graduated for .303, the No.8 has a .22lr graduated rear sight and the N9 has a single 25 yard datum mark on the left side of the sight which is otherwise a normal .303 calibrated No.4 sight. The Mk.1 aperture rear sights are micrometer adjustable with 'clicks' roughly equalling a 1 MOA elevation shift per 'click' which results in an approximate adjustment of 1" at 100 yards. The Mk.2 two position aperture sight has fixed apertures for 300 (bayonet fixed) and 600 yards (without bayonet). The Mk.3, Mk.4 and CMk.4 aperture sights are simplified stamped production and are adjustable in 100 yard increments from 200 to 1300 yards via a sliding scale with a fixed 300 yard (with bayonet fixed) battle sight.

The No.32 (Mk.1-3) and L1A1 sights found on the No.4 Mk.1(T) and L42A1 are mounted by two pads on the receiver accepting the quick-detach scope bracket which is secured by two thumb screws by the user. The optic is 3x magnification and the elevation drums are adjustable from 100-1000 yards. The windage is adjustable 16 MOA left and right in 2 MOA clicks on the MK.1 and 1 MOA clicks on the MK.2&3. On the Mk.1 scopes, the elevation is adjustable in 50 yard increments. On the Mk.2&3 they are click adjustable in 1 MOA increments. The range scales on all No.32 scopes are in yards.

On the L42A1, the sights (optics on the L1A1 scope and flip up aperture sights) have had their range graduations changed to meters as well as being calibrated for the 7.62 NATO cartridge. This is normally visible either by a 'M' marking on the turret of the L1A1 scope or a 'M' marking in the top corner of the flip up rear sight (the marking can sometimes be found on the side of the moving aperture piece on the sight).

The learner can demonstrate this by:

Verbal explanation, written description, or online test if available.

To teach this lesson, the trainer needs:

- Live, drill purpose or suitable deactivated firearms.
- (optional) Various sight types as examples.

2.5 Lee-Enfield Rifles

The learner will: **Understand the characteristics of the weapon.**

The learner can: **Adjust the sight setting using the correct tools.**

The learner knows:

☒ Handle

To adjust the tangent sight on the No.1 Mk.1-Mk.III* the user must depress the button on the side of the sight and move the unit forwards or backwards along

☑ Use

☑ Competent

the scale until the indicator on the slight block matches the desired range increment on the scale where the button can then be released which secures the sight in place. The foresight should only be adjusted by an armourer.

The aperture rear sights are micrometer adjustable with 'clicks' roughly equalling a 1MOA elevation shift per 'click' which results in an approximate adjustment of 1" at 100 yards.

The No.32/L1A1 scope is adjusted for windage and elevation in the same manner by the user adjusting the drum to line up with the desired windage or elevation increment.

Safe Use of Small Arms – Lee-Enfield Rifles

The learner can demonstrate this by:

Demonstration (drill purposes or deactivated rifle with moving parts may be suitable) or online test if available.

To teach this lesson, the trainer needs:

- Live, drill purpose or suitable deactivated firearms.
- (optional) Various sight types as examples.

2.6 Lee-Enfield Rifles

The learner will: **Understand the characteristics of the weapon.**

The learner can: **Explain the types of ammunition used with the weapon system.**

The learner knows:

There are four main ammunition types that are commonly encountered: ball, blank, drill and inert. Other types, such as tracer and armour piercing are unlikely to be encountered and specialist advice must be sought before their use.

☑ Handle

☑ Use

☑ Competent

Lee-Enfield rifles are most commonly chambered using .303-inch British Service ammunition. However, they may be found in other calibres either converted or produced in official service (including 7.62mm ammunition) and unofficial conversions for sport or target shooting.

AMMUNITION TYPES MUST NEVER BE MIXED.

Ball ammunition consists of a cartridge with a bullet. This is the standard type of ammunition in service and is designed to **kill**. Shown is a rimmed .303-inch cartridge.

Blank ammunition is a cartridge that does not have a bullet. It is used to simulate the noise and flash of a ball round. The energy created when fired means it is still **lethal** at close range and **must not** be fired with any person less than 30 yards in front of the weapon.

Drill rounds are specifically designed and manufactured to simulate the size and shape of ball ammunition. It does not contain any explosive propellant or primer. It is safe to use. Drill rounds contain a bullet that can sometimes become detached

from the body of the round so must be inspected before and after use to ensure all components are intact and present.

Inert ammunition is used to simulate ball ammunition for display purposes, particularly those seeking historical accuracy. It is usually made from spent cases of ball or blank and inserting a new bullet but without propellant or a primer. It can be

difficult to identify whether a round is truly inert, especially if a dummy or 'oiled' primer has been used so it does not look like it has been struck by a firing pin. Indicators that a round is inert can include a struck primer (although this could indicate a faulty primer in ball ammunition), an inspection hole drilled in the side or a ball-bearing inside the round to show it is empty. Extra care must be taken with unstruck primers as they may only be 'oiled', and these are shown to still contain explosive energy after they have supposedly been treated. **Under no circumstances shall undrilled inert ammunition be loaded into any firearm**.

Other terms used to describe ammunition include **live, spent**, or **dummy**. **Live** is *often* used to describe **ball** ammunition but could also mean unfired **blank** ammunition. **Spent** would generally indicate that it is the empty cases of **ball** or **blank** ammunition. **Dummy** could mean **blank, drill** or **inert**. The use of the correct terminology is important to avoid any confusion when handling items, therefore:

Live indicates the state of unfired ammunition irrespective as to whether it is **ball** or **blank**. The use of Live when describing ammunition must be accompanied by a further term such as Live Ball or Live Blank

Spent is fired ammunition irrespective as to whether it is **ball** or **blank**.

Dummy should not be used to describe any ammunition and it should always be clarified.

Ammunition for the Lee-Enfield Rifles is loaded either via chargers or as individual rounds into the magazine.

Chargers with rimmed ammunition (such as .303-inch) are loaded in the 'down and up' configuration as pictured below. Chargers using rimless ammunition have a simple 'flat' configuration but require an insert into the charger bridge to function correctly, with the exception of the Indian 2A and 2A1 rifles which are machined from the factory to take the flat chargers.

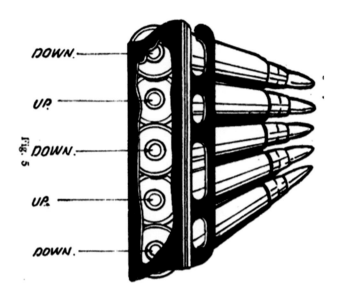

The learner can demonstrate this by:

Verbal explanation, written description, or online test if available.

To teach this lesson, the trainer needs:

- (optional) An example of each ammunition type.
- (optional) .303 and 7.62 chargers.

2.7 Lee-Enfield Rifles

The learner will: **Understand the characteristics of the weapon.**

The learner can: **Fit and remove ancillaries in line with operational procedures.**

The learner knows:

The Lee-Enfield Rifles have numerous accessories and ancillaries associated with them. This element includes those with which it is most commonly used.

☒ Handle

☒ Use

☑ Competent

Bayonets:

On No.1 rifles, the bayonet is secured to the rifle by lining up the lug on the nose cap of the rifle to the corresponding catch on the butt of the bayonet as well as ensuring the loop on the bayonet at the base of the blade is lined up with the corresponding lug on the nose cap found just below the muzzle. To secure the bayonet, the user should (by holding the handle of the bayonet) pull the bayonet downwards to secure it on to the rifle. When properly secured a 'click' sound should be heard. It is essential to verify the bayonet has seated correctly by holding the handle and trying to remove the bayonet without depressing the release catch. To remove the bayonet, the user should take hold of the handle of the bayonet and depress the release catch found at the base of the hand and pull the bayonet away from the rifle.

On No.4 pattern Lee-Enfield rifles, the bayonet attaches via a socket that contains a sprung plunger. To fit the bayonet, the socket needs to be placed on to the muzzle at a 60 degree angle with the blade in the 3 o'clock position where the user pushes down on the socket and rotates the bayonet 60 degrees, so the blade sits under the muzzle (6 o'clock position). To remove the bayonet, the user depresses the catch at the rear of the bayonet then performs the attachment movement in reverse.

On No.5 Mk.1 rifles, the same principle as the No.1 rifle's bayonet fitting applies with the exception the bayonet is seated over the conical flash

hider on the No.5 instead of a designated bayonet lug.

Sling and sniper rifle sling:

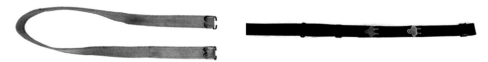

The standard sling most commonly found on the Lee-Enfield rifles is of canvas construction and is fitted to the rifle by feeding the brass end of the sling through the sling swivels and the feeding the sling under the tabs on the sling to secure it. The brass ends should sit on the inside of the sling closest to the rifle.

The sling commonly found on sniper rifles is the American pattern 1907 leather sling. The sling is secured to the rifle by two brass ends both with a pair of 'claws' which similarly to the canvas sling, are fed through the sling swivel and connect to the rifle by two hooks which can be inserted into any of the existing holes on the sling, the hole selected determines the length of the sling.

Breech Cover:

The breech cover is designed to keep dirt and debris away from the bolt and receiver when the rifle is not in use. To fit the cover to the rifle, the user must ensure all of the press studs are open, the cover can then be placed over the receiver and the press studs closed which secures the cover to the rifle.

No.32/L1A1 Scope:

This passage only applies to the No.4 Mk.1(T) and L42A1 sniper rifles. The No.32/L1A1 scope can be removed and installed via two thumb screws located on the scope bracket. To install the scope to the rifle, the scope bracket needs to be lined up with the corresponding scope pads on the receiver and the two thumb screws tightened in a clockwise direction 'finger tight' with no need for a tool to be used. To remove, the thumbscrews are turned anti-clockwise until the scope and bracket comes free form the action pads.

The learner can demonstrate this by:

Demonstration (drill purposes or deactivated rifle with moving parts may be suitable) or online test if available.

To teach this lesson, the trainer needs:

- Sling (various patterns).
- (optional) Bayonet (various patterns).
- (optional) Breech Cover.
- (optional) No.32/L1A1 scope.

3.1 Lee-Enfield Rifles

The learner will: **Understand the working parts of the weapon.**

The learner can: **Conduct NSPs in line with organisational procedures.**

The learner knows:

⊠ Handle

That they are required to conduct NSPs when they take the Lee-Enfield rifles from any storage, have been absent from it at any point or at the start of any period working with the weapon.

⊠ Use

☑ Competent

REFER to NSPs for Lee-Enfield Rifles – *See* Appendix 1.

The learner can demonstrate this by:

Weapons Handling Test 1.

To teach this lesson, the trainer needs:

- Live, drill purpose or suitable deactivated firearm.
- (optional) Drill rounds.

3.2 Lee-Enfield Rifles

The learner will: **Understand the working parts of the weapon.**

The learner can: **Explain the main parts of the weapon.**

The learner knows:

⊠ Handle

This section is a development of Element 2.3 and the learner should be able to explain these in the context of how the Lee-Enfield Rifles operate.

⊠ Use

☑ Competent

They will be assessed on this Element during their assessment for Element 3.3.

The learner can demonstrate this by:

Verbal explanation, written description, or online test if available.

To teach this lesson, the trainer needs:

- Live, drill purpose or suitable deactivated firearm.
- (optional) Skeletonised rifle.

3.3 Lee-Enfield Rifles

The learner will: **Understand the working parts of the weapon.**

The learner can: **Describe the internal mechanism of the weapon.**

The learner knows:

☒ Handle

Closing the bolt and chambering a round:

☒ Use

☑ Competent

Starting from an open bolt with a full magazine (magazine cut-off open if present) the user pushes the bolt forwards where the head of the bolt picks up a cartridge where the nose of the cartridge slides up the feed ramp getting guided into the chamber with the rim of the cartridge sliding under the extractor claw in the process. In the final stage of closing the bolt the cocking piece is pressed against the sear which cocks the rifle as the Lee-Enfield systems are cock on close (with the exception of the No.8). The closing of the bolt also rotates the rear locking lugs into the locked position. For single shot .22 rimfire Lee-Enfields, a round is placed directly into the chamber as there is no magazine to feed from (The No.7 is the only .22 rimfire Lee-Enfield with a magazine concerned by this publication).

Firing the rifle:

If the safety is in the rearward position it needs to be rotated forwards into the fire position, once this is done, the user depresses the trigger through both stages which drops the sear allowing the striker to move forwards and strike the primer firing the round.

Opening the bolt after firing:

Lifting the bolt handle upwards rotates the locking lugs out of the locked position. Pulling the bolt rearwards extracts the fired case from the chamber with friction from the sidewall of the receiver ejecting the case or in the case of a live or drill round, until the bolt is far enough back where the ejector engages on the case to eject it from the action.

The learner can demonstrate this by:

Verbal explanation, written description, or online test if available.

To teach this lesson, the trainer needs:

- Live, drill purpose or suitable deactivated firearm.
- (optional) Drill rounds.

4.1 Lee-Enfield Rifles

The learner will: **Be able to load and unload the weapon.**

The learner can: **Conduct NSPs in line with organisational procedures.**

The learner knows:

☑ Handle

That they are required to conduct NSPs when they take the Lee-Enfield Rifle from any storage, have been absent from it at any point or at the start of any period working with the weapon.

☑ Use

☑ Competent

REFER to NSPs for Lee-Enfield Rifles – See Appendix 1.

The learner can demonstrate this by:

Weapons Handling Test 1.

To teach this lesson, the trainer needs:

- Live, drill purpose or suitable deactivated firearm.
- (optional) Drill rounds.

4.2 Lee-Enfield Rifles

The learner will: **Be able to load and unload the weapon.**

The learner can: **Load the weapon.**

The learner knows:

How to be able to respond to the following orders when under the supervision or control on a range. They may also operate independently; however, they would be expected to follow the same sequence of orders and procedures.

☒ Handle

☑ Use

☑ Competent

Prior to firing, it is necessary to conduct preliminary checks and preparation of the Lee-Enfield Rifles (*see* Element 7.5).

In this element, there are three separate orders: **Load**, **Ready**, and then a **Fire** order. This is in compliance with the current MOD requirements for range management; however, other ranges may operate differently and the **Load** may also imply **Ready** or **Load and Make Ready** may be given as the command. The user should ensure that they are conducting their drills in accordance with any local range requirements.

Load

(Note: **Load** only applies to magazine-fed rifles. Single-shot do not require the **Load** command and either a **Load and Make Ready** should be used or the user waits until the **Make Ready** command is given).

The user pushes forward the safety catch (if applied), opens the magazine cut-off (if present), fully opens the bolt (if not already open), inserts the charger into the charger guide and depresses the rounds from the charger into the magazine. This is repeated twice to enable a full magazine of 10 rounds to be loaded.

If a charger is not being used or is not able to be used (e.g. on sniper variants with an overbore scope) the user will load individual rounds into the rifle by placing them on top of the magazine in the receiver and applying pressure on to the round until it is retained by the magazine. It is advisable to place the round slightly forward in the magazine and sliding it backwards to prevent any issues caused by overlapping rims. This process is repeated 10 times to fill the magazine or less if the user does not wish to fill the magazine. For the magazine fed No.7, a magazine of 5 (or less depending on the course of fire) rounds would be inserted into the rifle.

Leave the bolt open and await further instructions.

Ready

Close the bolt to chamber a round and rotate the bolt downwards at the end of its travel to lock the bolt and cock the striker.

For single shot rifles, a single round would be manually loaded into the chamber and the bolt closed.

Apply the safety catch (move it to the rear) and await further instructions.

Fire

Depending on the circumstances, there may be a fire control order given. This may include:

- Designation (who is to do the firing – it may not be **you**),
- The range (which must then be set on the sight – *see* Element 2.4),
- An indication of the target (which should be confirmed and the target acquired),
- The method of fire
- The command **Fire.**

Upon completing the procedure for laying the rifle on the target and acquiring it as outlined in the fire control order, upon the command **Fire**, the user checks their aim is on target (adjusting if not), places the safety in the forward position and depresses the trigger to fire.

During the course of fire, the user must listen for any instructions from the Range Conducting Officer.

The learner can demonstrate this by:

Weapons Handling Test 2.

To teach this lesson, the trainer needs:

- Live, drill purpose or suitable deactivated firearm.
- Drill rounds.

4.3 Lee-Enfield Rifles

The learner will: **Be able to load and unload the weapon.**

The learner can: **Make the weapon safe.**

The learner knows:

How to respond to the following orders when under the supervision or control on a range. They may also operate independently; however, they would be expected to follow the same sequence of orders and procedures.

☒ Handle

☑ Use

☑ Competent

A **Make Safe** command may be given for several reasons or at different stages in a course of fire. For example, when an incident occurs elsewhere on the range that requires the Range Conducting Officer's attention, but it does not require a full **Unload**, activity in the butts of a gallery range or awaiting a different section of the course of fire to be prepared. Use of the **Make Safe** is at the discretion of the Range Conducting Officer.

If the command **Make Safe** is received, then the user should disengage the safety (if engaged); withdraw the bolt to eject any round or case; close the bolt on an empty chamber by using the cutoff or pushing down on the top round and carefully easing the bolt forward; take a dry shot in a safe direction, apply the safety catch.

Await further instructions, which will likely be a **Ready** or **Unload** order.

The learner can demonstrate this by:

Weapons Handling Test 3.

To teach this lesson, the trainer needs:

- Live, drill purpose or suitable deactivated firearm.
- Drill rounds.

4.4 Lee-Enfield Rifles

The learner will: **Be able to load and unload the weapon.**

The learner can: **Unload the weapon.**

The learner knows:

☒ Handle

How to be able to respond to the following orders when under the supervision or control on a range. They may also operate independently; however, they would be expected to follow the same sequence of orders and procedures.

☑ Use

☑ Competent

At the completion of firing, it is necessary to **Unload** the weapon. This may be commanded by a range control officer or supervisor following a **Make Safe** (*see* Element 4.3) or at the completion of the task.

Open the bolt and pull it to the rear to eject any spent case or unfired round. If any rounds remain in the magazine, they can be removed by either pulling out the cutoff (if present and engaged), the bolt can then be pushed forwards until the next round in the magazine is caught by the extractor claw and the bolt then drawn backwards which ejects the round from the magazine and rifle. This process can be repeated until the magazine is empty (NSP 4). It is worth noting the bolt only needs travel about 50% of the length of the magazine to allow a round to be ejected and the bolt must not be turned down when ejecting the rounds.

Alternatively, the user can remove the magazine from the rifle and remove the rounds from the magazine (with the empty magazine inserted back into the rifle if required).

The **Unload** is then likely to be followed by presenting the weapon as clear (*see* Element 4.6) or completing the NSPs.

It is also necessary to conduct specific post-firing maintenance (see Element 7.5).

The learner can demonstrate this by:

Weapons Handling Test 4.

To teach this lesson, the trainer needs:

- Live, drill purpose or suitable deactivated firearm.
- Drill rounds.

4.5 Lee-Enfield Rifles

The learner will: **Be able to load and unload the weapon.**

The learner can: **Place chargers or rounds within pouches (or magazines if dictated by range or competition rules).**

☑ Handle

The learner knows:

☑ Use

That upon the completion of any use of ammunition, the ammunition (usually in charger) must be returned to a safe and clean place, such as the user's ammunition pouch, bandolier or other container.

☑ Competent

This ensures that the ammunition is stored safely and unlikely to become damaged or dirty. It should be visually inspected as it is returned to the container and any misplaced rounds reinserted into a charger.

The learner can demonstrate this by:

Weapons Handling Test 4 or online test if available.

To teach this lesson, the trainer needs:

- Live, drill purpose or suitable deactivated firearm.
- Drill rounds.
- Chargers.
- Appropriate pouches or containers.

4.6 Lee-Enfield Rifles

The learner will: **Be able to load and unload the weapon.**

The learner can: **Prove the weapon for inspection (for inspection port arms).**

The learner knows:

☑ Handle

That to prove the weapon is in a safe condition, they are required to conduct the Normal Safety Precautions for the Lee-Enfield Rifles in a similar manner to when handing over or taking over the weapon (Element 1.6)

☑ Use

☑ Competent

Note: The final state of the weapon will depend on the local range regulations and the user must ensure they are familiar with them.

When requested to prove the weapon for inspection, or at the end of a period of firing or other training, it is necessary to demonstrate the weapon is clear of any ammunition and is in a safe condition.

To present the weapon as safe, conduct NSPs 3 to 5.

At this point the firer should raise their hand to indicate the weapon is clear to the range conducting officer. If there is not a range conducting officer present, then they can carry on with the procedure.

Once inspected or confirmed clear, NSPs 6 to 10 can be completed.

In some circumstances, it may be necessary to keep the weapon in a state where it is obviously safe to a casual observer:

* Bolt open and to the rear with magazine empty of any rounds

For added visibility and to comply with local range regulations (if required), a breech flag may be inserted in the barrel with the flag pointing horizontally down the barrel with the flag visible in the receiver and in some cases where required, the magazine may need to be removed from the receiver.

REFER TO NSPs for Lee-Enfield Rifles – *See Appendix I.*

The learner can demonstrate this by:

> Demonstration (drill purposes or deactivated rifle with moving parts may be suitable) or online test where available.

To teach this lesson, the trainer needs:

- Live, drill purpose or suitable deactivated firearm.
- (optional) Drill rounds.
- (optional) Breech flag.

5.1 Lee-Enfield Rifles

The learner will: **Be able to conduct stoppage drills.**

The learner can: **Conduct NSPs in line with organisational procedures.**

The learner knows:

☒ Handle

That they are required to conduct NSPs when they take the Lee-Enfield Rifle from any storage, have been absent from it at any point or at the start of any period working with the weapon.

☑ Use

☑ Competent

REFER TO NSPs for Lee-Enfield Rifles – *See* Appendix I.

The learner can demonstrate this by:

Weapons Handling Test I.

To teach this lesson, the trainer needs:

- Live, drill purpose or suitable deactivated firearm.
- (optional) Drill rounds.

5.2 Lee-Enfield Rifles

The learner will: **Be able to conduct stoppage drills.**

The learner can: **Explain the main causes of weapon stoppages.**

The learner knows:

They need to be able to identify the main causes of stoppages with the Lee-Enfield Rifles so they can rectify them in a safe and efficient manner.

☒ Handle

☑ Use

☑ Competent

There are two main types of stoppages: **temporary** and **prolonged**.

Temporary are due to:

- Faulty ammunition
- Error in operation of the rifle

Prolonged are due to failure of some part which cannot, as a rule, be put right by the team without skilled assistance.

It is temporary stoppages for which an 'immediate action' can be performed.

- Rim-jam: where the rims of the cartridges in the magazine are overlapping and the rims catch on each other preventing the bolt from moving forward
- Bolt will not close on a round of ammunition: if the bolt cannot close easily or with a slight amount of pressure:
    - o The ammunition is deformed
    - o The bolt or chamber has excessive fouling/dirt
- A round of ammunition does not fire
- A round of ammunition is not chambered

The learner can demonstrate this by:

Verbal explanation, written description, or online test if available.

To teach this lesson, the trainer needs:

- Live, drill purpose or suitable deactivated firearm.
- (optional) Drill rounds.

5.3 Lee-Enfield Rifles

The learner will: **Be able to conduct stoppage drills.**

The learner can: **Explain the immediate action (IA) drills for stoppages.**

The learner knows:

The immediate action (IA) drills vary depending on the type of stoppage incurred (*see* Element 5.2).

☒ Handle

☑ Use

☑ Competent

- Rim jam: the first action would be to smack the bolt forwards hard, if this does not rectify the issue, the user should depress the rounds in the magazine down as far as possible and let go sharply. If this fails, the user can use their hand to remove the overlapping rims in the magazine
- Bolt will not close on a round of ammunition:
  - o The ammunition is deformed: eject the round of faulty ammunition and do not return to where ammunition is kept keeping the defective round(s) separate
  - o The bolt or chamber has excessive fouling/dirt: the user can check for any clearly visible obstructions preventing the bolt from closing and clear them
- A round of ammunition does not fire:
  - o The user can retract the cocking piece to the cocked position where they can then try again to fire the round, if it does not fire on the second attempt, 30 seconds should be allowed to pass and then the round may be ejected and regarded as defective.
- A round does not enter the chamber
  - o Draw back the bolt
  - o Press rounds into magazine and release them suddenly

- o Ensure the magazine is correctly fitted by tapping the bottom of the magazine sharply
- o The user should cycle the bolt again in order to feed a round into the chamber

The learner can demonstrate this by:

Verbal explanation, written description, or online test if available.

To teach this lesson, the trainer needs:

- No special equipment.

5.4 Lee-Enfield Rifles

The learner will: **Be able to conduct stoppage drills.**

The learner can: **Conduct IA drills to clear stoppages.**

The learner knows:

☒ Handle

The correct IA drills for the stoppages listed in Element 5.3 and will be able to demonstrate them.

☑ Use

☑ Competent

The learner can demonstrate this by:

Demonstration (drill purposes or deactivated rifle with moving parts may be suitable) or online test where available.

To teach this lesson, the trainer needs:

- Live, drill purpose or suitable deactivated firearm.
- (optional) Drill rounds.
- (optional) Special drill rounds to simulate stoppages (damaged case, thick rim or damaged rim for example).

5.5 GENERIC

The learner will: **Be able to conduct stoppage drills.**

The learner can: **Explain the procedure for damaged rounds caused by stoppages.**

Defective ammunition must be stored away from all other spent casings or live ammunition. As with defective weapons (see Element 1.3), it must be reported to the Authority Holder and include:

☒ Handle

☑ Use

☑ Competent

- The manufacturer.
- The batch.
- A description of how it was being used.
- Any damage caused to the weapon, ancillaries or any injuries to persons.

If being used on a managed range, the Range Conducting Officer must be informed, and the local procedures followed as necessary. This may include reports as described above.

The learner can demonstrate this by:

Verbal explanation, written description, or online test if available.

To teach this lesson, the trainer needs:

- No special equipment.

6.1 Lee-Enfield Rifles

The learner will: **Be able to strip and assemble the weapon.**

The learner can: **Conduct NSPs in line with organisational procedures.**

The learner knows:

⊠ Handle

That they are required to conduct NSPs when they take the Lee-Enfield Rifles from any storage, have been absent from it at any point or at the start of any period working with the weapon.

⊠ Use

☑ Competent

REFER to NSPs for Lee-Enfield Rifles – *See Appendix 1.*

The learner can demonstrate this by:

Weapons Handling Test 1.

To teach this lesson, the trainer needs:

- Live, drill purpose or suitable deactivated firearm.
- (optional) Drill rounds.

6.2 Lee-Enfield Rifles

The learner will: **Be able to strip and assemble the weapon.**

The learner can: **Explain the importance of using the correct tools for stripping and assembling the weapon.**

☒ Handle

The learner knows:

☒ Use

Despite the generic title of this element, **no** tools should be used for stripping and assembling as part of the routine maintenance of the rifle.

☑ Competent

To perform a basic field strip and reassembly of a Lee-Enfield Rifle, no tools are needed.

The learner can demonstrate this by:

Verbal explanation, written description, or online test if available.

To teach this lesson, the trainer needs:

- No special equipment.

6.3 Lee-Enfield Rifles

The learner will: **Be able to strip and assemble the weapon.**

The learner can: **Strip the weapon and ancillaries for inspection.**

The learner knows:

The rifle is stripped in the following order.

Parts should be laid out in the order of stripping.

☒ Handle

☒ Use

☑ Competent

No.1 and No.2 Mk.IV Rifles:

The bolt is opened and pulled to the rear most point of travel where the bolt head should be pushed upwards with enough pressure to overcome the retaining spring. Once the bolt head is released and rotates freely within the receiver, it should be rotated to the 12 o'clock position where the bolt is then pulled rearwards removing it from the rifle. The bolt head should be unscrewed and removed. The magazine can then be removed by depressing the magazine catch in the trigger guard and pulling the magazine away from the receiver. Reassembly is the reverse process, it is important to fully screw in the bolt head and then back it off slightly to align with the rib of the bolt.

No.4 Mk.1, Mk.2, Mk.1/2, No.5, No.7, No.7 & N9 Rifles:

The bolt is opened and pulled to about 1cm from the rear most point of travel where the bolt catch should be depressed (and held down) with one hand before pulling the bolt to the end of travel (with the catch still depressed). The bolt head can then be rotated into the 12 o'clock position where the bolt can then be pulled rearwards removing it from the rifle. In most cases, the rear sight will need to be in the upwards position to remove the bolt (most sniper rifles have sights with a relief cut to allow the bolt to be removed without the sight being raised). The bolt head should be unscrewed and removed. The magazine can then be removed by depressing the magazine catch in the trigger guard and pulling the magazine away from the receiver. Reassembly is the reverse process, it is important to fully screw in the bolt head and then back it off slightly to align with the rib of the bolt.

Further stripping may be required but should be completed under supervision of an armourer or other competent person.

No.4 Mk.1*, Mk.1/3 Receiver Rifles:

The bolt is opened and pulled rearwards to where the bolt head aligns with the slot in the receiver track. When aligned, the bolt head can be rotated to the 12 o'clock position and the bolt pulled rearwards out of the receiver (rear sight must be in the raised position). The bolt head should be unscrewed and removed. In most cases, the rear sight will need to be in the upwards position to remove the bolt (most sniper rifles have sights with a relief cut to allow the bolt to be removed without the sight being raised). The magazine can then be removed by depressing the magazine catch in the trigger guard and pulling the magazine away from the receiver. Reassembly is the reverse process, it is important to fully screw in the bolt head and then back it off slightly to align with the rib of the bolt.

Further stripping may be required but should be completed under supervision of an armourer or other competent person.

The learner can demonstrate this by:

Weapons Handling Test 5.

To teach this lesson, the trainer needs:

- Live, drill purpose or suitable deactivated firearm.

6.4 Lee-Enfield Rifles

The learner will: **Be able to strip and assemble the weapon.**

The learner can: **Assemble the weapon and ancillaries.**

The learner knows:

To assemble, reverse the order of stripping.

The learner can demonstrate this by:

    Weapons Handling Test 5.

To teach this lesson, the trainer needs:

- Live, drill purpose or suitable deactivated firearm.

☒ Handle

☒ Use

☑ Competent

6.5 Lee-Enfield Rifles

The learner will: **Be able to strip and assemble the weapon.**

The learner can: **Confirm the operation of the weapon.**

The learner knows:

Following the completion of stripping and assembling, the learner should demonstrate the function of the weapon. They can do this by completion of the NSPs.

☒ Handle

☒ Use

☑ Competent

The learner can demonstrate this by:

Weapons Handling Test 5.

To teach this lesson, the trainer needs:

• Live, drill purpose or suitable deactivated firearm.

7.1 Lee-Enfield Rifles

The learner will: **Be able to clean and maintain the weapon.**

The learner can: **Conduct NSPs in line with organisational procedures.**

The learner knows:

That they are required to conduct NSPs when they take the Lee-Enfield Rifles from any storage, have been absent from it at any point or at the start of any period working with the weapon.

REFER to NSPs for Lee-Enfield Rifles – *See* Appendix 1.

The learner can demonstrate this by:

Weapons Handling Test 1.

To teach this lesson, the trainer needs:

- Live, drill purpose or suitable deactivated firearm.
- (optional) Drill rounds.

☒ Handle

☒ Use

☑ Competent

7.2 Lee-Enfield Rifles

The learner will: **Be able to clean and maintain the weapon.**

The learner can: **Explain the effects of adverse climatic/environmental conditions on the weapon system.**

The learner knows:

Adverse climatic conditions include: hot, dry, sandy or dusty; cold and extreme cold; hot, wet; and, marine.

☒ Handle

☒ Use

☑ Competent

This qualification is focussed on use in the United Kingdom; however, there are weather extremes present that could affect firing the weapon.

Hot, dry, sandy or dusty

In these conditions, the weapon can overheat more frequently in these conditions. Rust can form quicker due to the fluctuations in temperature (particularly between night and day). Weapon accuracy can be affected by temperature, particularly at longer ranges. Metal parts may become extremely hot. Lubrication will evaporate more quickly.

Specific control:

- Great care is necessary in the quantity of oil to be used. A thin film of oil, meaning parts wiped over with a slightly oiled rag, will prevent rust forming during the night and also be sufficient lubricant for working the rifle during firing.

Cold and extreme cold

Parts may become more brittle in cold or freezing conditions.

Specific controls:

- Oil the mechanism very slightly.

Hot, wet

As with hot dry, overheating and evaporation will occur more quickly. Rust is a particular concern and frequent lubrication is required.

Marine

This environment includes those areas near the coast, particularly coastal firing ranges where salt spray or sea air is present. This causes rust and corrosion quicker so re-lubrication and thorough cleaning is required.

The learner can demonstrate this by:

Verbal explanation, written description, or online test if available.

To teach this lesson, the trainer needs:

- No special equipment.

7.3 Lee-Enfield Rifles

The learner will: **Be able to clean and maintain the weapon.**

The learner can: **Explain the contents of the weapon cleaning kit.**

The learner knows:

☒ Handle

The weapon cleaning kit contains few items and can be found in the butt of the rifle or carried in a separate container.

☒ Use

☑ Competent

The main items included are:

- Pull-through
- Brush
- Gauze (should not be used due to abrasive nature causing damage to the rifle)
- Flannelette
- Oil bottle, may contain a spoon or brush

Additional specialist items include the chamber cleaning stick, cleaning rod and a water funnel.

The learner can demonstrate this by:

Verbal explanation, written description, or online test if available.

To teach this lesson, the trainer needs:

- Weapon cleaning kit.

7.4 Lee-Enfield Rifles

The learner will: **Be able to clean and maintain the weapon.**

The learner can: **Clean the weapon using the weapon cleaning kit.**

The learner knows[5]:

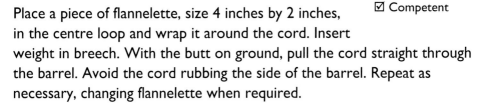

☒ Handle

Cleaning the barrel:

☒ Use

☑ Competent

Place a piece of flannelette, size 4 inches by 2 inches, in the centre loop and wrap it around the cord. Insert weight in breech. With the butt on ground, pull the cord straight through the barrel. Avoid the cord rubbing the side of the barrel. Repeat as necessary, changing flannelette when required.

Examine bore by holding muzzle close to the eye, draw head back and look into grooves for dirt. Repeat from breech end. If barrel is clean, oil it with flannelette 4 inches by 1 inch. Should dirt still be present (as it may be after firing) use water if available.

Use of water (optional, unless corrosively-primed ammunition has been used): Pour 5 to 6 pints of water (boiling if possible) carefully through barrel, using a funnel or any other suitable appliance; boiling water is best, hot water is better than cold, but even cold water is better than no water at all. This will remove corrosive substances and, if boiling, can aid the removal of non-ferrous metal deposits. Dry, examine and oil the barrel.

Cleaning the chamber:

Use a stick about a foot long with a slot at the top for flannelette. A piece of flannelette 4 inches by 2 inches should be inserted and wrapped around

---

[5] War Office, *Pamphlet 3: Small Arms Training Volume 1* (His Majesty's Stationery Office, 1942).

the stick which is then pushed hard into the chamber and turned several times.

Note. - The best accuracy of fire is obtained if the barrel and chamber are dried before firing.

Cleaning the outside of the rifle:

After cleaning barrel and chamber, wipe the dirt from all metal portions, using an oily rag. Make certain all crevices and gas escapes are clean.

Cleaning the magazine:

Remove dirt from inside and outside, if necessary, remove platform and spring by pressing down wide end. Narrow end is then disengaged from front lips. Remove platform and spring carefully. Replace in reverse order. It should only be removed when necessary.

The learner can demonstrate this by:

Weapons Handling Test 5.

To teach this lesson, the trainer needs:

- Live, drill purpose or suitable deactivated firearm.
- Suitable cleaning kit.

7.5 Lee-Enfield Rifles

The learner will: **Be able to clean and maintain the weapon.**

The learner can: **Maintain the weapon in line with operational requirements.**

The learner knows:

There are three key periods for weapons maintenance during use: **before, during** and after **firing**. This is preventative and restorative and ensures the weapon is properly maintained.

☒ Handle

☒ Use

☑ Competent

They must be completed before any firing, whether ball or blank.

There is also routine maintenance outside of the use of the rifle.

Before firing

- Dry out the barrel
- Examine and clean all parts before assembly
- Oil necessary parts and surfaces

During pauses in firing

- Ensure all parts are functioning as intended with no parts becoming loose or misaligned e.g. magazine not seated correctly, or rear sight knocked out of the vertical position (if applicable)

After firing finished (on firing range)

- Unload
- Clean the barrel
- Clean the chamber

When back in camp

- Strip and clean all parts
- Examine all parts for wear and damage

Regular maintenance in store

Depending on the environment, the rifle may need re-oiling whilst in storage.

The learner can demonstrate this by:

Verbal explanation, written description, or online test if available.

To teach this lesson, the trainer needs:

- Live, drill purpose or suitable deactivated firearm.
- Suitable cleaning kit.

Appendix I – Normal Safety Precautions

Lee-Enfield Rifles

The purpose of Normal Safety Precautions (NSPs) is to render a weapon with an unknown or unsafe state into a known safe state.

This is a fundamental element of all firearms handling and should be mastered prior to progressing any further in the training.

☑ Handle

☑ Use

☑ Competent

	**1. Safe Direction** Ensure the firearm is pointed in safe direction.
	**2. Safety Off** Push forward the safety catch to the 'off' position.

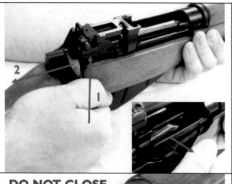

3. Open Bolt

Lift the bolt handle up and pull to the rear.

DO NOT CLOSE FULLY

REPEAT UNTIL CLEAR

4. Cycle Until Clear

Keeping the bolt handle up, move the bolt handle forwards to push forward rounds from the magazine into the chamber but DO NOT move forward fully and DO NOT close the bolt handle down. Repeat until the magazine is EMPTY.

Or the user can remove the magazine.

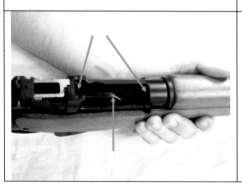

3-Point Check

Visually inspect the magazine well, chamber and bolt face for any rounds or evidence of remaining rounds.

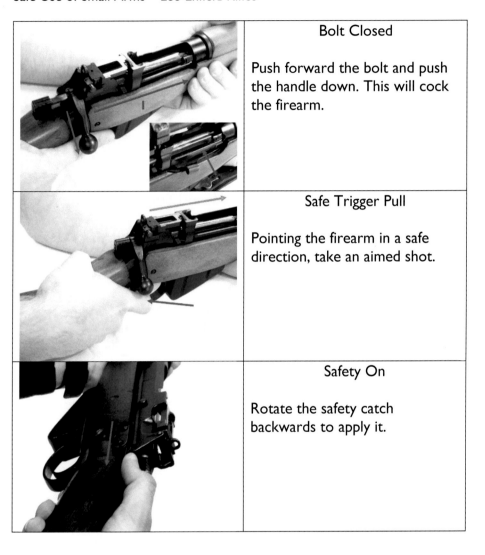

	Bolt Closed Push forward the bolt and push the handle down. This will cock the firearm.
	Safe Trigger Pull Pointing the firearm in a safe direction, take an aimed shot.
	Safety On Rotate the safety catch backwards to apply it.

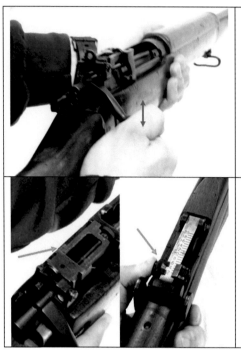	**Bolt Secure** Check the safety catch is working correctly by attempting to raise the bolt handle.
	Sights to 200 For consistency and preparation for future use, set the sights to 200 where possible.

Appendix 2 – Firing Record

As part of the Safe Use of Small Arms system operated by the VMGCRA, Firing Records are maintained for each individual firearm and must be completed on any occasion the firearm is used. A copy must be kept with the firearm and used for barrel and component life analysis as part of any firearms inspection (see Appendix 5).

SAFE USE OF SMALL ARMS 3
LEE-ENFIELD RIFLES
(ALL MARKS)

FIRING RECORD (WEAPON)

GUN S.N.:   BARREL S.N.:

DATE	FIRER	ROUNDS FIRED		CASUALTIES	REMARKS	RCO / SUPERVISOR
		BALL	BLANK			

© Vickers MG Collection
& Research Association 2023
www.vickersmg.org

SHEET NUMBER ......

These drills form part of a wider training system and must not be used in isolation.

Appendix 3 – Assessment Plan

For the successful completion of this course, the learner must be assessed. Obtaining knowledge in isolation of assessment does not enable the skills to be verified. Therefore, the following plan indicates the stages at which a learner will be assessed and determined as **safe to handle, safe to fire, competent**. The **currency** of the competence will be assessed at least annually with increases depending on frequency of use.

For the VMGCRA, this will determine the level of independence given to the learner.

This also provides an indicative course of progressive training.

Safe to handle (assessed by instructor)**:**

Required for firers and handlers.

Elements 1.1 to 1.5, 2.1, 2.6, 4.1, 4.5, 4.6.

☑ Handle
☑ Use
☑ Competent

Safe to use (assessed by instructor and assessor):

Required for firers.

Elements 1.1 to 1.5, 2.1, 2.4 to 2.6, 4.1 to 4.6, 5.1 to 5.5.

☒ Handle
☑ Use
☑ Competent

Competent (assessed by instructor and assessor):

Required for firers.

All Elements.

☒ Handle
☒ Use
☑ Competent

Trainer and **Armourer** levels require applied knowledge of all elements and appendices.

Appendix 4 – Weapons Handling Tests

To be carried out to demonstrate the competency of an individual. These should be completed at least annually but more regularly if the individual does not regularly use the weapon.

Test 1 – Safety

☑ Handle

The individual must demonstrate, and narrate, the completion of the Normal Safety Precautions on a Lee-Enfield Rifle – a deactivated example is suitable if the weapon functions sufficiently.

☑ Use

☑ Competent

On being instructed to carry out the Normal Safety Precautions, the individual should complete them, narrating their actions using the correct terminology and following the sequence of actions shown in Appendix 1 of this book.

To successfully pass this test, the individual must complete the Normal Safety Precautions. They may be permitted some errors in sequence if they do not present a safety risk. Furthermore, slight errors in terminology may be permitted as long as the individual is clear in their meaning.

Safety fails (0 permitted):

- Not pointing in a safe direction
- Finger on trigger or trigger pulled before 3-point check has been carried out

Test 2 – Load, Ready, Fire

☒ Handle

The individual must demonstrate the safe loading of the Lee-Enfield Rifles. It requires a functional weapon and drill ammunition.

☑ Use

☑ Competent

The rifle should have the bolt closed on a fired striker with safety applied and ammunition to hand or stored in pouches on the shooter's person.

On the command '**Load**' the individual must Load the weapon in accordance with Element 4.2 of this book.

On the command '**Ready**' the individual must **Ready** the weapon in accordance with Element 4.2 of this book.

The assessor will issue a Fire Control Order, using an artificial or natural aiming mark as available, and the individual will then lay the rifle on that mark with the range adjusted to the issued order.

Safety fails (0 permitted):

- The rifle is not correctly laid on the range and mark indicated.
- The drill is not followed correctly.

Procedural fails (2 permitted):

- The user performs some steps out of order

Test 3 – Make Safe

☒ Handle

The individual must demonstrate making safe the Lee-Enfield Rifles. It requires a functional weapon and drill ammunition.

☑ Use

☑ Competent

The weapon should be in the **Ready** or **Fire** state prior to conducting the test.

Safety fails (0 permitted):

- The drill is not followed correctly.
- User's fingers are on the trigger or in the trigger guard when making safe

Procedural fails (2 permitted):

- The individual follows the Unload drill with an immediate 'Show Clear' or conducts the Normal Safety Precautions.

Test 4 – Unload

☒ Handle

The individual must demonstrate the safe unloading of the Lee-Enfield Rifles. It requires a functional weapon and drill ammunition.

☑ Use

☑ Competent

The weapon should in the **Load, Ready,** or **Fire** state prior to conducting the test.

On the command '**Unload**' the individual must **Unload** the weapon in accordance with Element 4.4 of this book.

Safety fails (0 permitted):

- The drill is not followed correctly.

Procedural fails (2 permitted):

- The individual follows the Unload drill with an immediate 'Show Clear' or conducts the Normal Safety Precautions.

Test 5 – Stripping, Cleaning and Assembling

☒ Handle

The individual must demonstrate, and narrate, the complete stripping, cleaning and assembling of the Lee-Enfield Rifles. It requires a functional weapon and equipment as described in Element 7.3.

☒ Use

☑ Competent

The rifle should be in an unloaded and safe state with the bolt open prior to the test.

The rifle must be stripped in the correct order as described in Element 6.3 and the parts laid out. As the individual is stripping the rifle, they should narrate the process using the correct terminology for any parts they handle. The assessor should question the individual if their narration is not forthcoming.

Upon successful completion of the rifle being stripped, it should be cleaned to a suitable standard. The individual may identify points for further cleaning if time doesn't allow it to be done during the test.

At the end of the assembly, they must confirm the operation of the weapon in line with Element 6.5.

Safety fails (0 permitted):

- The individual places any part of their hands, fingers, etc in any position that would cause them harm.
- Fail to confirm the operation of the weapon.

Procedural fails (2 permitted):

- Each occasion the assessor has to assist the individual in any aspect of the stripping, cleaning or assembling is considered a separate error.
- Each error in terminology is considered a separate error.

Appendix 5 – Instructions for Armourers

The purpose of this section is to provide sufficient detail that enables a competent armourer to inspect a Lee-Enfield rifle and ensure it is mechanically sound and in sufficiently good condition to conduct manned firing. It is written with the Ministry of Defence's requirement for inspection of Non-Service Pattern Light Weapons in mind (Ministry of Defence, 2020).

As with the Weapons Firing Record produced as part of the SUSA system, a Weapon Inspection Record form is also produced to record the relevant information as required in the MOD policy and guidance.

SAFE USE OF SMALL ARMS 3
LEE-ENFIELD RIFLES
(ALL MARKS)

INSPECTION RECORD

GUN S.N.:   BARREL S.N.:

Date	CHS	FPP	Bore Go	Bore No Go	General Condition	Average 25m group size	Sentence	Rounds Fired (see firing record)	Signature

© Vickers MG Collection
& Research Association 2023
www.vickersmg.org

SHEET NUMBER ......

MOD Note: This form is an alternative layout to Annex H3 of DSA 03.OME Part I (JSP 520) and contains all relevant information and should be read in conjunction with the Firing Record.

General Condition

To assess the general condition of the rifle, it is important to inspect the following areas, the order of inspection below can be followed:[6]

- Remove bayonet and scabbard, check any serial number and log number on bayonet and also on rifle
- Check serial number on body against bolt, backsight, nosecap, fore-end. Remove pull-through and oil bottle
- Rifle in vice at point of balance. Test with .064" and .074" headspace gauges (applied to .303 only). Test for weight or looseness of retaining spring
- Remove bolt and magazine
- Remove rifle from vice, examine barrel (using bullet) for freedom at the muzzle, both ends for straightness, cleanliness, cuts, bulges, metallic fouling, damaged or rusty chamber
- Examine sights, foresight for damage of blade, straightness, tightness of block and blade. Backsight for tightness of leaf/body, freedom of leaf/body, straightness and clearance from protector, damage to 'U' or aperture, correct functioning of slide/elevation mechanism, damage to sight leaf/body
- Examine ejector screw and safety catch. Check if the ejector screw is broken or damaged (some 7.62 conversions **may** not have an ejector screw). Verify if the safety catch locking bolt is broken or worn and if the safety catch locking bolt spring works or is weak
- Examine the handguards, nosecap, fore-end, butt, butt plate. Check the handguard for any splits or warping. Nosecap for any erosion or burrs. Fore-end for any splits, damage and general fit. Butt for any splits, damage, looseness and condition of the butt swivel. Buttplate for any damage to the trap and freedom of the trap

---

[6] Swindon, Vickers MG Collection & Research Association, Course Notes: Rifles, No. 1, Mks. III & III*, V10673.29.1.

- Place rifle in bench or in a vice and test screws for tightness (when placing the rifle in the vice it should not be clamped across the receiver, only on the butt or the mid-point between the receiver and the middle barrel band
- Examine the magazine for dents, distortion of lips, freedom of the follower, tightness and serviceability of the follower and springs. Fit magazine back into the rifle
- Examine the bolt for any broken or damaged parts. Condition of screws on the cocking piece and bolt head. Check for any burrs or wear on the cam face. Any fractures or pitting on the bolt, freedom of the striker, clearance of the striker from the bolt and any looseness of the cocking piece. Bolthead with excessive overturning (should overturn by around 20 degrees), bolthead pitted (especially face), broken or worn hook on the extractor, bolt lever damaged length and radius of the striker using gauge
- Examine the safety stud on the cocking piece for any damage
- Replace the bolt into the rifle, test the magazine fitment and cut-off (if present) using 10 drill rounds, test for extraction and ejection. Test the safety functionality
- With the rifle in the vice, test for weights of springs and pull-off
- Remove rifle from vice and reassemble
- Examine bayonet and scabbard for cleanliness, straightness of blade, damage by improper use, grips and screws for condition, bolt for functioning and nut bolt for tightness and leather (if present) for condition
- Examine rifle for general condition of the woodwork
- Examine pull-through for serviceability

High Pressure Proof

Proof marks on the Lee-Enfield rifles are typically found under the handguard on the top of the barrel. There can be some exceptions to this where another country or civilian proofs have been placed elsewhere.

There are also differences in the case of the 7.62mm conversions (L42A1, L39A1, 7.62 Conv, Envoy, Enforcer) which have additional proof marks on the bolt body and bolt head to indicate they have been proofed to 19 tonnes to handle the additional pressure of 7.62 ammunition. The mark is '19T' under crossed flags.

Weapon Examination[7]

<u>Barrel Bore Measurements</u>

No.1 and No.4/5:

The standard bore gauges for .303 are .301", .307", .310" and Gauge Lead No.2. Gauge plug should run through the bore to show freedom from bends, metallic fouling etc.

For a barrel to be determined to be serviceable on a .303, the gauges should be used in the following manner:

- Gauge plug .307" should not run through the barrel
- Gauge plug .308" should not enter the muzzle ¼ inch
- Gauge plug .310" should not enter the breech ½ inch
- Gauge lead No.2 should not enter the chamber ½ inch

The barrels should also be given a general visual inspection for bends, bulges, cuts, fouling, corrosion etc.

No.2 Mk.IV, No.7 No.8, N9:

Gauge bore with cylindrical acceptance plugs L.0.216 inch must run. The barrel should be free of any lateral influence by the fore-end.

7.62 models:

- With Inspectors plug 0.30in. Mk.1, the gauge must run for the full length of the bore

---

[7] Swindon, Vickers MG Collection & Research Association, Armament Wing, REME Training Centre. Armourers Section. Serial No. 1. Date: 19 Feb., 47. Equipment Notes. Subject: RIFLES, V10673.10.

- With Armourers, plug 0.306in. No.1 Mk.1, the barrel is rejected when the plug enters muzzle 0.25in
- With Armourers plug 0.307in. Mk.1, the barrel is rejected when the plug is accepted at breech more than 0.25in

Cartridge Headspace (CHS)

No.1:

The gauges required to test the rifle are:

- Gauges Armourers 0.64" No.1
- Gauges Armourers 0.74" No.1

The bolt should not close over the 0.74" gauge but should accept the 0.64" gauge. If the rifle accepts the 0.74" gauge a new bolt head must be fitted, and the test process is repeated.

Striker protrusion must always be checked after fitting a new bolt head.

No.2 Mk.IV, No.7 No.8, N9:

With the breech of the rifle closed, the space between the face of the bolt head and the breech face of the barrel should reject .005 in. slip gauge, and the .008 in, slip gauge should not enter without pressure.

No.4/5:

The gauges required to test the rifle are:

- Gauges Armourers 0.64" No.1
- Gauges Armourers 0.74" No.1

The bolt should not close over the 0.74" gauge but should accept the 0.64" gauge. If the rifle accepts the 0.74" gauge a new bolt head must be fitted, and the test process is repeated.

If headspace is incorrect in the rifle, Heads Bolt Breech are issued in varying sizes for easy adjustment. There are 4 sizes issued, marked 0, 1, 2, 3, each size varying by .003 inches. If headspace is excessive a higher numbered bolt head will be fitted, similarly if it is insufficient a lower number can be fitted.

Note: Lift and Striker Protrusion must also be in mind when adjusting headspace in this way.

7.62 models:

- With gauge U 2452 Low 1.629in (Extractor and spring removed, gauge placed in the chamber), the breech must close
- With gauge U 2453 High 1.634in (Extractor and spring removed, gauge placed in the chamber, the breech must not close

Firing Pin Protrusion (FPP)

No.1, No.4, No.5, No.7, No.8, N9:

The following gauges are required to test the striker protrusion:

- Gauges Striker Protrusion No. 1 - .040"L
- Gauges Striker Protrusion No. 1 - .050"H

To adjust striker protrusion: Should the striker be long, reduce the point of the striker; care being exercised to retain the correct radius at the point of .038", this radius is also on the gauge.

Should striker protrusion be insufficient, reduce the tenon of the head bolt breech; care being taken to keep it flat and square.

Note: The length of the tenon of the head bolt breech controls the "Lift", and so "lift" must be borne in mind when reducing.

No.2 Mk.IV(*):

The firing pin is gauged to the same limits as the striker point for Rifle No. 1. The firing pinpoint is radius .048 in. instead of .038 in.

To fit a New Firing Pin. Remove the bolt head and insert a new firing pin. In the fully forward position, the rear of the firing pin should not protrude beyond the tenon of the head bolt breech. The firing pin can be reduced at the rear end until it is just below the level of the end of the tenon. This ensures that the head bolt breech, and not, the firing pin arrests the forward movement of the striker.

7.62 models:

With gauge U 3997, (accept: 1.354, reject: 1.546), and the firing pin held in the forward position gauge applied to the striker point, the gauge must contact striker point or rock on 0.135mm, the point must not contact on 1.546mm.

The Vickers MG Collection & Research Association uses a wide variety of small arms in its demonstrations and events. Over time we will develop the following titles as part of the training for these:

1. Vickers Machine Gun (Mark I)
2. Bren Light Machine Gun
3. Lee-Enfield Rifle (SMLE to Enforcer)
4. Revolvers (British Service)
5. Sterling Sub-Machine Gun (all marks)
6. Thompson Sub-Machine Gun (all marks)
7. M1 Carbine
8. Mauser Rifles
9. Broomhandle Mauser
10. Shotguns (break-open)
11. Vickers .5-inch
12. MG42 (and variants)
13. Automatic pistols
14. AK series
15. Vickers Target Rifles
16. Shotguns (semi-automatic)
17. MP40
18. FN FALs (and variants)
19. M1 Garand
20. Sten Sub-Machine Guns

They can be ordered from:

https://vickersmg.blog/product-category/books/safe-use-of-small-arms/

OTHER TITLES AVAILABLE

A CANLOAN Officer
by R F Fendick

Postcards of the Machine Gun Corps
by VMGCRA

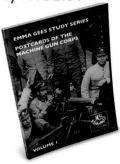

The Vickers Machine Gun
by Dolf L. Goldsmith

Over **900** pages!

Please check our shop for availability and prices.

As online prices vary, buy directly from us to be sure of the best price: **http://vickersmg.blog/shop** or scan the QR codes.

Our popular online shop stocks:
• books • clothing • mugs • educational courses
• manuals* • posters • militaria • parts

*selected manuals are free to download.